TUESDAY

DAVID WIESNER

A TRUMPET CLUB SPECIAL EDITION

TUESDAY EVENING, AROUND EIGHT.

TO TRUMPET CLUB FANS

LET YOUR IMAGINATION TAKE FLIGHT

FOR TOM SGOUROS

Illustrations executed in watercolor on Arches paper.
The type is Bulmer.

Published by The Trumpet Club
1540 Broadway, New York, New York 10036

Text and Illustrations copyright © 1991 by David Wiesner

ISBN 0-440-84639-0

This edition published by arrangement with
Clarion Books/Houghton Mifflin Company
Printed in the United States of America
September 1992

5 7 9 10 8 6 4

11:21 P.M.

4:38 A.M.

NEXT TUESDAY, 7:58 P.M.